Mystical Mazes

by Doris J. Kitchens
and Margaret M. Zeff

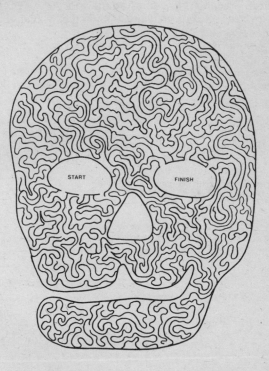

START   FINISH

Xerox Education Publications

Middletown, Connecticut

P9-ELP-732

This book is a presentation of
The Popcorn Bag

Weekly Reader Book Division offers book clubs for
children from preschool to young adulthood. All
quality hardcover books are selected by a distinguished
Weekly Reader Selection Board.

For further information write to:
Weekly Reader Book Division
1250 Fairwood Avenue
Columbus, Ohio 43216

THE TIMES TO BEAT

1. **Sun Spirlt** — 1:00 (1 minute)
2. **The Headless Horseman** — 1:00
3. **Wicked Witch of Willoughby** — 1:00
4. **Voodoo Mask** — 1:00
5. **Unlucky Thirteen** — 1:00
6. **Phantom of the Forest** — 1:15
7. **Demon's Delight** — 1:15
8. **Journey's End** — 1:15
9. **A Midnight Stroll** — 1:15
10. **Web of No Return** — 1:15
11. **Hoodoo Voodoo Doll** — 1:15
12. **Demon of the Dark** — 1:15
13. **Pharaoh's Return** — 1:30
14. **Hooded Head** — 1:30
15. **Fanged Fury** — 1:30
16. **Midnight Howl** — 1:30
17. **The Lonely Grave** — 1:30
18. **Moon Madness** — 1:30
19. **The Hanging Tree** — 1:30
20. **Star Power** — 1:30

THE TIMES TO BEAT (con t)

21. **Magic Castle** — 1:45
22. **Night Flier** — 1:45
23. **Merlin's Magic** — 1:45
24. **Witch Doctor** — 1:45
25. **The Witching Hour** — 1:45
26. **Night Wizard** — 1:45
27. **Haunted Mansion** — 1:45
28. **Restless** — 2:00
29. **The Evil Eye** — 2:00
30. **Graveyard Ghost** — 2:00
31. **Castle Caretaker** — 2:00
32. **Night Creeper** — 2:00

How to Solve a Mystical Maze

If you get a secret thrill and chill thinking about magical, mystical, supernatural things, then you won't even have to look into a crystal ball to find out that you'll have a whole witch's cauldron-ful of fun doing these eeeerie mazes. Just take pencil in hand and start right now to un-ravel these a-maze-ingly tangled webs. Begin each maze where "start" is shown. You must not cross over any of the solid lines. After you've weaved your way along the craggy paths to the finish line, you'll safely be home again (phew!) and will be ready to take on the next mysterious or scary journey.

For extra fun, see whether you can beat the challenge time given for each maze. One word of caution: do not be frightened out of your wits if the first maze you try seems devilishly hard. You may breeze through the next one as if by *mystical* magic!

Solutions are in the back of the book.

START

FINISH

Maze 1
SUN SPIRIT
Time to Beat / 1 minute

THE HEADLESS HORSEMAN

Time to Beat / 1 minute

WICKED WITCH OF WILLOUGHBY

Time to Beat / 1 minute

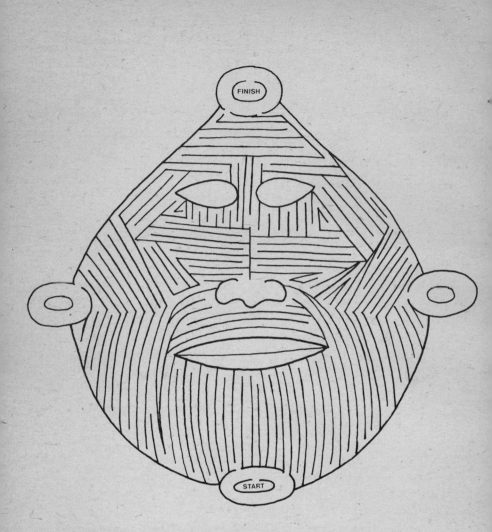

Maze 4
VOODOO MASK
Time to Beat / 1 minute

UNLUCKY THIRTEEN

Time to Beat / 1 minute

FINISH

START

Maze 6
PHANTOM OF THE FOREST
Time to Beat / 1 minute, 15 seconds

START

FINISH

JOURNEY'S END

Time to Beat / 1 minute, 15 seconds

A MIDNIGHT STROLL

Time to Beat / 1 minute, 15 seconds

Maze 10
WEB OF NO RETURN
Time to Beat / 1 minute, 15 seconds

HOODOO VOODOO DOLL

Time to Beat / 1 minute, 15 seconds

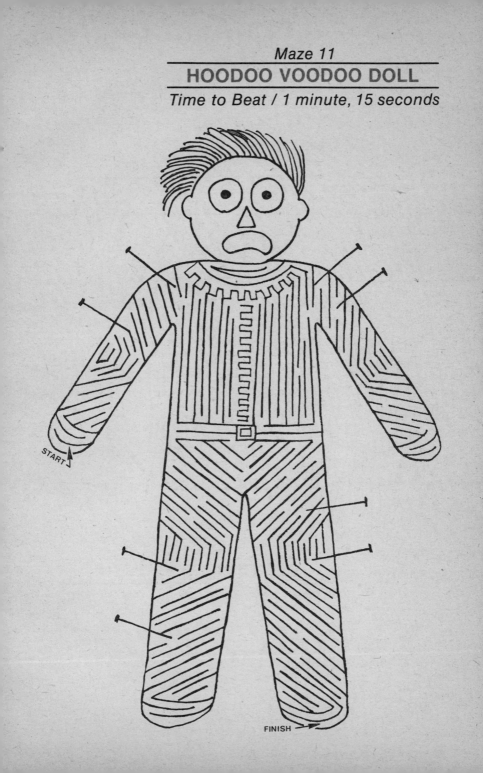

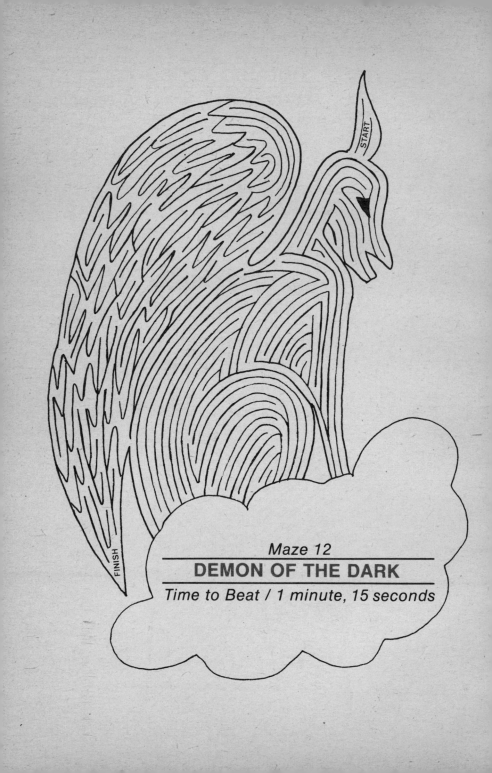

START

FINISH

Maze 12
DEMON OF THE DARK
Time to Beat / 1 minute, 15 seconds

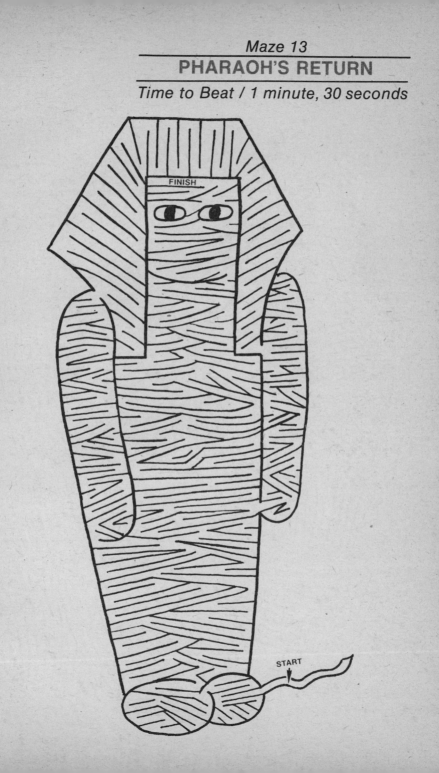

Maze 14
HOODED HEAD
Time to Beat / 1 minute, 30 seconds

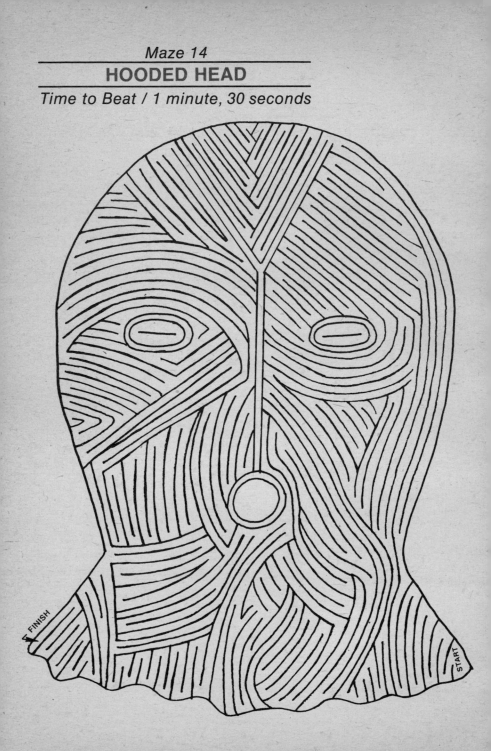

Maze 16

MIDNIGHT HOWL

Time to Beat / 1 minute, 30 seconds

Time to Beat / 1 minute, 30 seconds

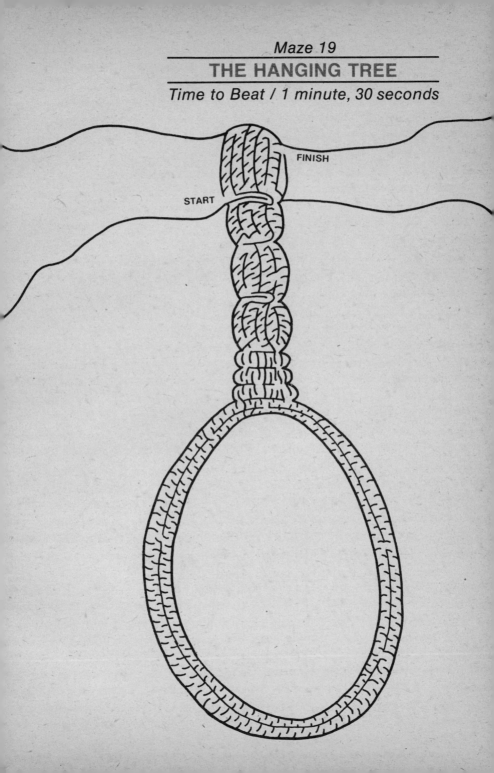

FINISH

START

STAR POWER

Time to Beat / 1 minute, 30 seconds

MAGIC CASTLE

Time to Beat / 1 minute, 45 seconds

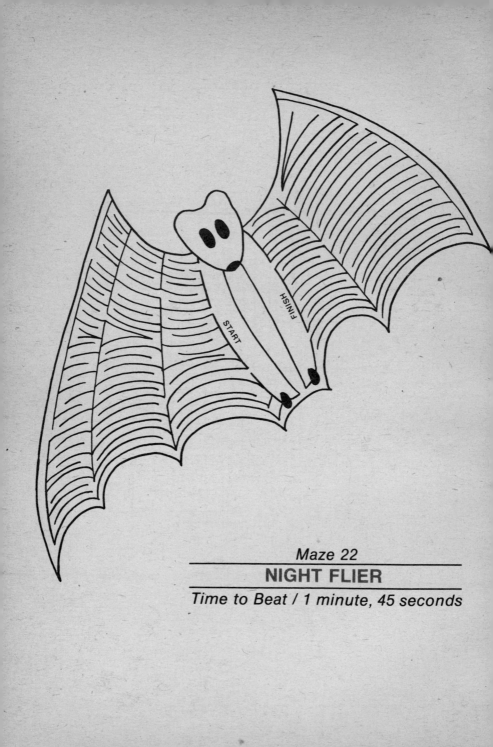

START

FINISH

Maze 22

NIGHT FLIER

Time to Beat / 1 minute, 45 seconds

THE WITCHING HOUR

Time to Beat / 1 minute, 45 seconds

START

FINISH

HAUNTED MANSION

Time to Beat / 1 minute, 45 seconds

Maze 28
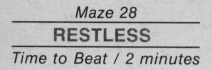
RESTLESS
Time to Beat / 2 minutes

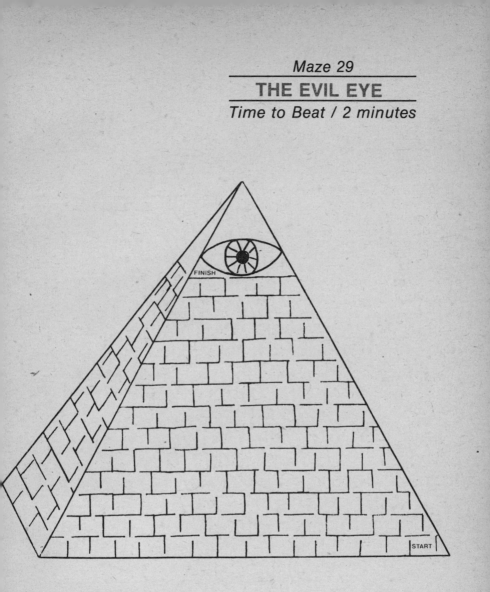

GRAVEYARD GHOST

Time to Beat / 2 minutes

CASTLE CARETAKER
Time to Beat / 2 minutes

START

FINISH

START

FINISH

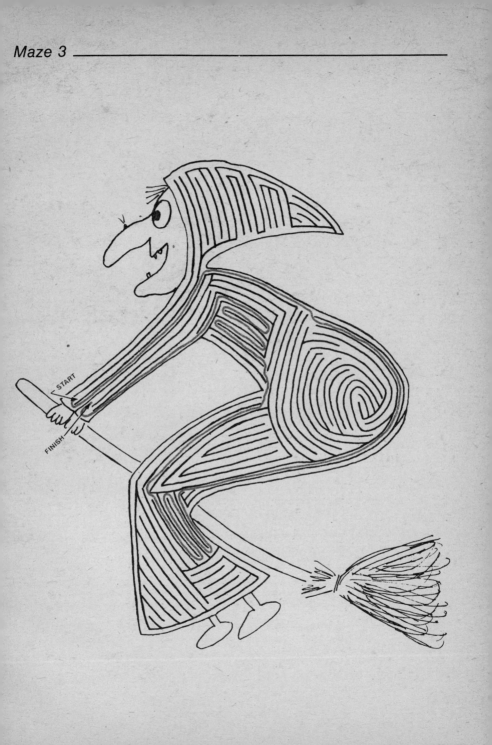

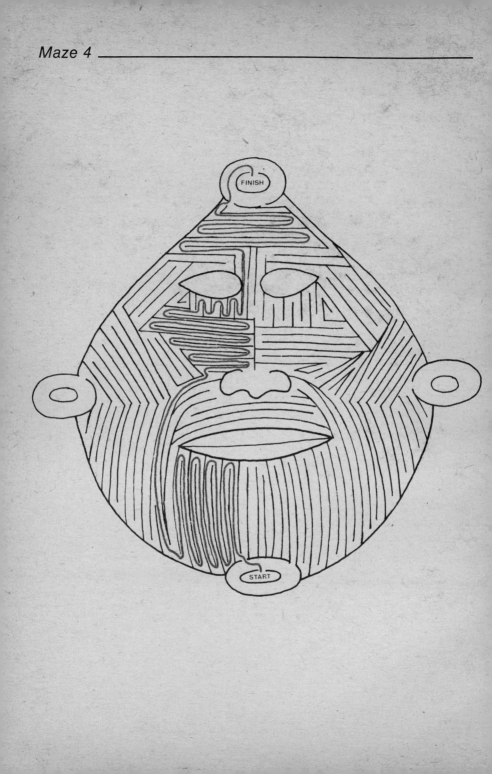

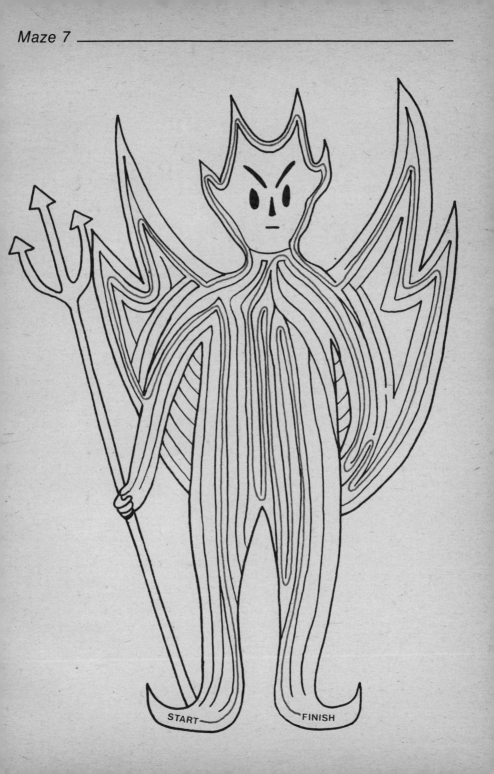

START FINISH

Maze 8

Maze 9

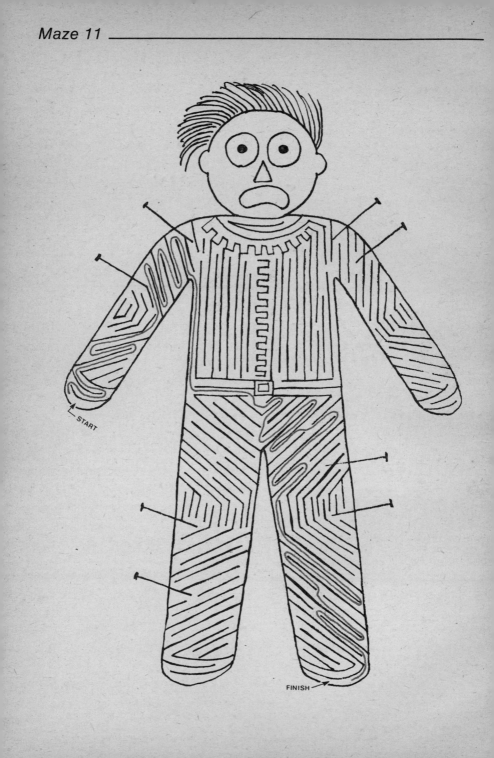

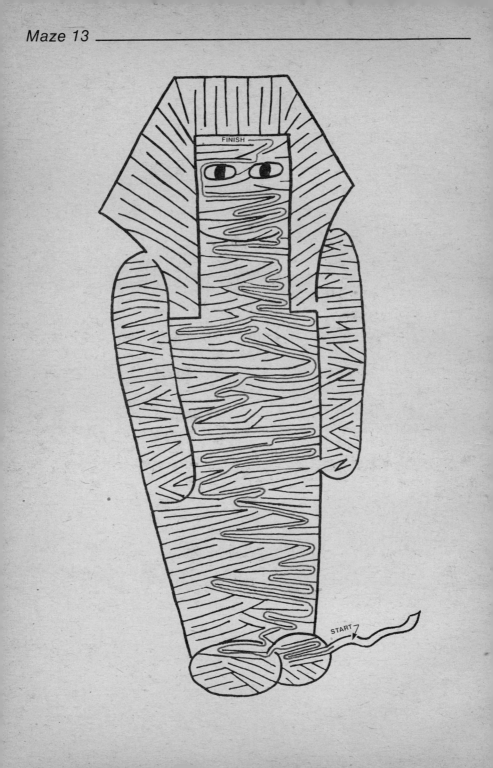

FINISH

START

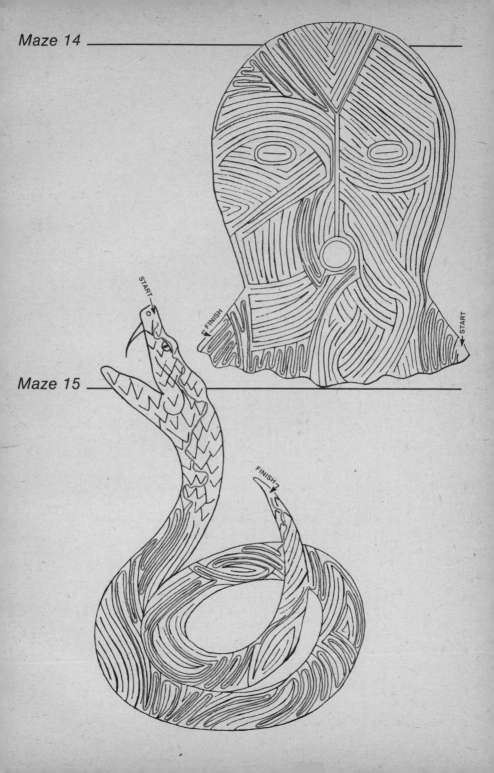

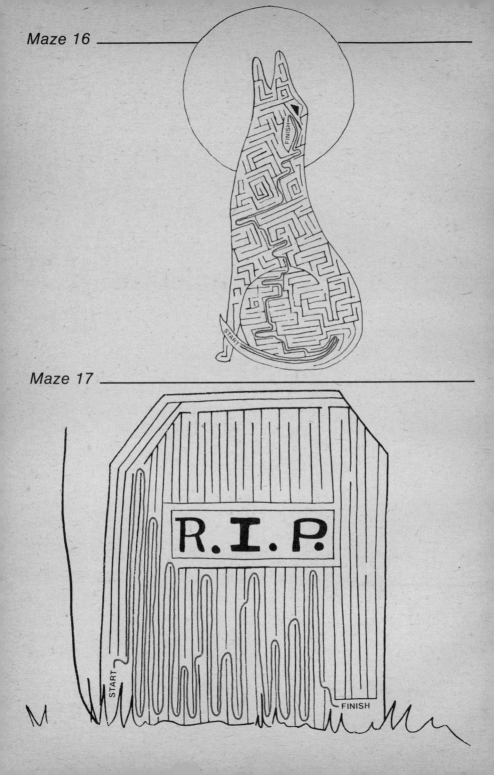

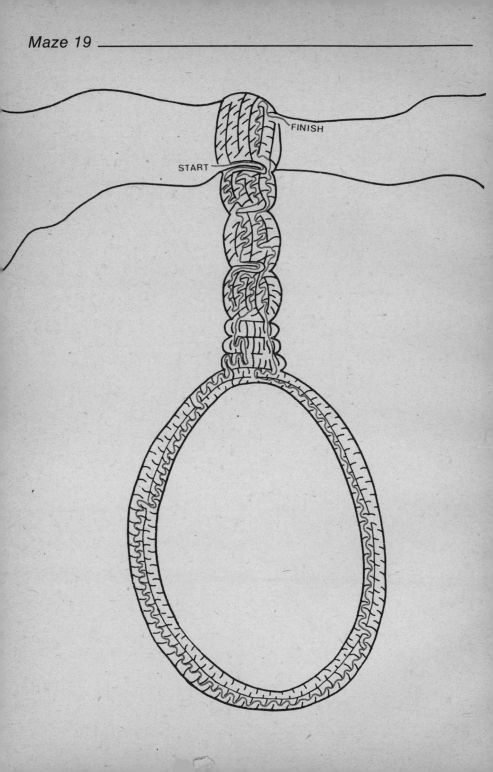

FINISH

START

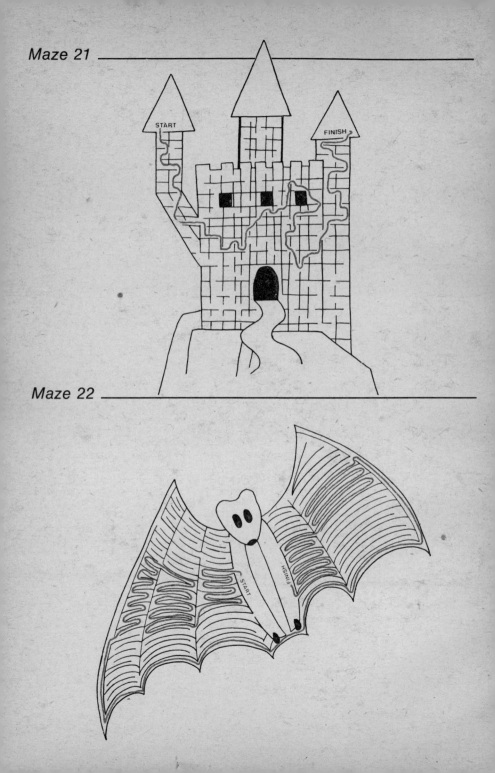

Maze 25 _____

START

FINISH

Maze 26 _____

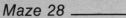

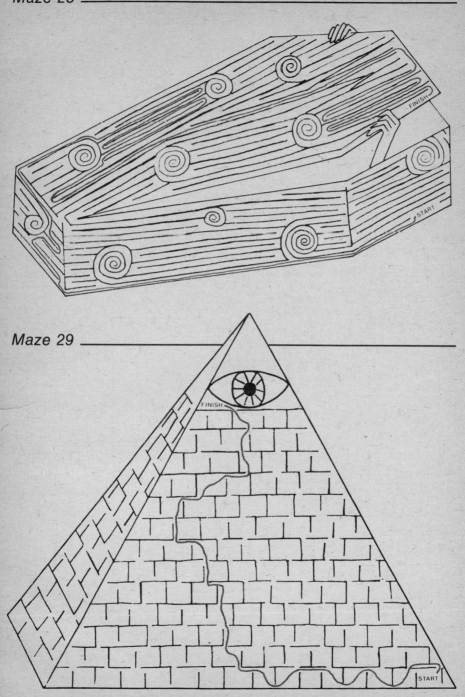

FINISH

START

Maze 29

FINISH

START

START

FINISH